# ECDL® Advanced 2.0

## Revision Series

## Module AM6

## Presentation

## using
## Microsoft® PowerPoint

**Release RS15v1**

# Revision Series

Published by:

CiA Training Ltd
Business & Innovation Centre
Sunderland Enterprise Park
Sunderland  SR5 2TA
United Kingdom

Tel: +44 (0) 191 549 5002
Fax: +44 (0) 191 549 9005

Email: info@ciatraining.co.uk
Web: www.ciatraining.co.uk

**ISBN 13: 978 1 86005 809 7**

First published 2009

CiA Training's **Revision Exercises** for **Advanced ECDL** contain a collection of revision exercises to provide support for students. They are designed to reinforce the understanding of the skills and techniques which have been developed whilst working through CiA Training's **AM6 -Presentation** book.

*This practice material, which has been approved by ECDL Foundation, includes exercise items intended to assist Candidates in their training for an ECDL Certification Programme. These exercises are not ECDL Foundation certification tests.  For information about authorised Test Centres in different national territories, please refer to the ECDL Foundation website at* www.ecdl.org

**Advanced Presentation** - The revision exercises cover the following topics, grouped into sections:

- Preparation
- Images and Drawn Objects
- Charts
- Multimedia
- Slide Shows
- Linking

*A minimum of two revision exercises is included for each section. There are also general exercises, which cover techniques from any section of this guide. Answers are provided at the end of the guide wherever appropriate.*

## The Revision Exercises are suitable for:

- Any individual wishing to practise advanced features of this application. The user completes the exercises as required. Knowledge of *PowerPoint* is assumed, gained for example from working through the corresponding **AM6 - Presentation** book produced by **CiA**.

- Tutor led groups as reinforcement material. They can be used as and when necessary.

## Downloading the Data Files

The data associated with these exercises must be downloaded from our website: *www.ciatraining.co.uk/data_files*. Follow the on screen instructions to download the data files.

By default, the data files will be downloaded to the **CIA DATA FILES\Advanced ECDL Revision\AM6** folder in either **My Documents** or **Documents** depending in your version of *Windows*.

The data required to complete the exercises is in the **Data** folder and worked solutions for every exercise can be found in the **Solutions** folder.

If you prefer, the data can be supplied on CD at an additional cost. Contact the Sales team at *info@ciatraining.co.uk*.

## Aims and Objectives

To provide the knowledge and techniques necessary to be able to successfully tackle the features of an advanced word processing application. After completing the exercises the user will have experience in the following areas:

- Creating and adding slides of various kinds to a presentation
- Changing colour schemes and background effects
- Using clip art and drawing tools
- Manipulating images
- Adding animation, sound and video clips
- Creating and editing charts, flowcharts and other diagrams
- Creating and running flowcharts
- Creating links to objects outside the presentation
- Producing custom slide shows

## Office Versions

These revision exercises were written without references to any specific office version. The data is, however, Office specific and the correct set of data should be downloaded to match your office version.

## Requirements

These revision exercises were created for *Microsoft PowerPoint*. They assume that the computer is already switched on, that a printer and mouse are attached and that the necessary programs have been fully and correctly installed on your computer. However, in *PowerPoint*, some features are not installed initially and a prompt to insert the *Office CD* may appear when these features are accessed.

The following revision exercises are divided into sections, each targeted at specific elements of the Advanced ECDL syllabus. The individual sections are an exact match for the sections in the ECDL Advanced Training Guides from CiA Training, making the guides an ideal reference source for anyone working through these exercises.

## Preparation

These exercises include topics taken from the following list: knowing how to plan a presentation including audience, venue and timing considerations , how to use colour schemes, using background colours and effects, creating, saving and using a template, using a word processed outline for text, inserting slides.

## Exercise 1

1. Which of the following may be reasons why different versions of the same presentation would be required?

   a) Audiences with different levels of technical competency

   b) Audiences with different areas of specialist interest

   c) Different length presentations required

   d) All of the above

2. What effect does slide design and appearance have on audience perception of a presentation?

   a) Not at all, content is everything

   b) Minimal, as long as content is clear

   c) Major, can affect how content is viewed

   d) Total, content is irrelevant

3. Give one advantage and one disadvantage of using dramatic images as backgrounds to a presentation?

4. Why might you need to limit fonts and moving items when showing a presentation to a visually impaired audience?

5. State two considerations when choosing colour combinations to use on slides.

6. State 3 factors which may need to be considered when looking at the venue for your presentation.

7.  Which of the following statements is true?

    a) You can change the colours in a colour scheme

    b) Each Design Template has only one possible colour scheme

    c) All slides in a presentation must have the same colour scheme

    d) Colour schemes depend on slide layout

8.  If you are asked to give your presentation in a limited time, with not enough time to see all slides for their allocated timing, what is the best solution?

    a) Talk faster

    b) Get as far through the presentation as you can in the time

    c) Create a shorter summarised version of the show

    d) Refuse to do it.

## Exercise 2

1.  Open the **Cruises** presentation from the data files. This consists of a slide master, a title master and one title slide.

2.  Apply the image **Boat** so that it will be the background image to any title slide in the presentation. Why does the colour scheme now need to be changed?

3.  Change the pre-set colour scheme for all master slides to one that has pale blue titles and white text.

4.  View the slide master and apply a background fill effect. Select a gradient effect from the **preset** list , e.g. **Nightfall**. Make sure the effect is applied to the slide master only.

5.  Delete the footer placeholder, move the number placeholder to the centre and insert a number in the centre of the placeholder.

6.  Save the presentation as a template called **Cruises**, but make sure it is saved in your data file folder, <u>not</u> in the default **Templates** folder.

7.   Now create a presentation based on this template. Insert all the slides from the **Sailing** presentation into the current presentation, making sure they take on the correct formatting.

8.   Apply a different design template/theme to slide 3 <u>only</u>. (if using *PowerPoint 2000* change the design for the entire presentation).

9.   Save the presentation as **Cruises2** and close it.

## Exercise 3

1.   Open the **Rocky** presentation from the data files. This consists of a slide master, a title master and one title slide.

2.   Apply the image **Rocky** so that it will be the background image to any title slide in the presentation.

3.   Edit the current colour scheme so that the title text on all slides will be a very dark blue. Make sure the change is applied to all masters.

4.   Apply a background fill effect that will be applied to all non title slides only. Select the **Parchment** texture effect.

5.   Create a custom slide master with the texture **white marble** as a background.

6.   Insert the image **Rockylogo** so that it will appear on every <u>non title</u> slide in the presentation (in *PowerPoint 2007* you will have to omit the image from the Title Slide Master). Enlarge it slightly and move it to the right edge of the title area.

7. Create four new slides in the presentation by importing text from the outline document **Rockytext.doc**, making sure they take on the correct formatting.

8. Apply the custom slide master to slides **3** and **5**.

9. Change the background for slide 5 so that the **Rockylogo** graphic is omitted from this slide only.

10. Save the presentation as **Rocky2** and close it.

## Images and Drawn Objects

These exercises include topics taken from the following list: working with drawn objects, changing object backgrounds, rotating and flipping images, selecting multiple objects, arranging objects, cropping and editing images.

## Exercise 4

1. Open the presentation **Camping**. You are to create a revised logo for the Rocky Valley Camping Site.

2. Add a new slide to the end of the presentation with a **Blank** layout. In the centre of the slide, draw an **Isosceles Triangle** from the basic shapes (hold down the <**Shift**> key as the shape is being drawn).

3. Add a **Fire** preset colour gradient background to the triangle. If this is not available use a simple gradient, yellow at the top to dark red at the bottom.

4. Apply any 3-D effect to the shape, and apply a surface setting of **Metal**.

5. Right click the new object and save the image as **Newlogo.gif**.

6. Change the logo on all slide masters by replacing it with **Newlogo**. Position the image so that it is **20cm** from the left edge and **0.8cm** from the top edge of the slide. Resize it so that it is 3cm high.

7. Delete the new slide from the end of the presentation.

8. Save the presentation as **Camping2** and close it.

## Exercise 5

1. Open the presentation **Camping**. Insert the only slide from the **Eagle** presentation at the end of the **Camping** presentation.

2. Insert the image **Eagle.jpg** into the new slide.

3. Crop the image to include only the eagle's head. As a guide, the final image should be about **5cm** square.

4. Move the image to the right of the text. Use a tool from the picture toolbar (in the **Adjust** group in *2007*) to make the majority of the blue sky above the eagle's head transparent.

5. Increase the contrast by **3** levels and then apply a **Washout** appearance to the image.

6. Use copy and paste to create another copy of the altered image on the slide.

7. Ensure the snap to grid feature is on. Flip the new copy horizontally and move it to the left of the text.

8. Align the two images and the text so that their bottom edges line up and they are evenly distributed horizontally.

9. Align the two images and the text so that they are centred vertically on the slide.

10. Save the presentation as **Camping3** and close it.

## Exercise 6

1.  Open the presentation **Egypt Tours**.

2.  View the slide master and display the ruler.

3.  Create a logo for the company. In the top right corner of the slide master, draw an isosceles triangle about **3cm** by **3cm**.

4.  Colour the background with a preset **Desert** gradient effect.

5.  Make this background the default for all new shapes drawn.

6.  Apply a **Parchment** background effect to all slides in the presentation.

7.  The logo is too big. Maintaining the original proportions, rescale the triangle to approximately **2cm** by **2cm**.

8.  Ensure it is still in the right corner of the title area.

9.  On slide **3**, increase the contrast of the image of Tutankhamun's death mask by **3** levels, then reduce the brightness by **3** levels.

10. Save slide **4 Great Pyramid** as an image in **.png** format, named **cheops.png**.

11. On slide **1** recolour the red part of the graphic to green. Note that this will involve **ungouping** the image and converting it to a drawing object.

12. Save the presentation as **Tours** and close it.

## Charts

These exercises include topics taken from the following list: creating combination charts/2 axes charts, editing charts, creating flowcharts and other diagrams, editing flowcharts, animating charts.

## Exercise 7

1. Start a new presentation containing a blank **Title Only** slide. Add a title of **Product Testing**.

2. Create the following flowchart using shapes from the **Flowchart** and **Connectors AutoShapes**. Use text boxes for the **Yes/No** captions.

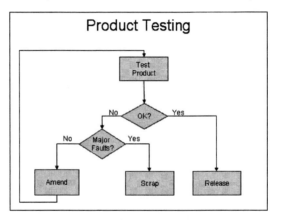

3. Amend the top box of the flow chart to be white text on a dark blue background.

4. Use the **Format Painter** tool to apply this style to all the other flowchart shapes.

5. Change all elbow connectors to **Curved Arrow Connectors**.

6. Insert a new, blank slide with a **Title and Content** layout and add the title **Product Sales**.

7. Create a cycle diagram and add the processes **Market Research**, **Targeted Marketing** and **Sales Results**.

8. Change the colours/style of the diagram as desired.

9. Save the presentation as **Diagrams** and close it.

## Exercise 8

1. Open the presentation **Chart**. The chart shows the year's turnover and profit for a company. Because of the large difference in values, it is difficult to compare them.

2. Change the chart type to **Lines**.

3. Convert this to a **2 Axes** chart type by selecting the **Profit** data series and formatting it to be plotted on a secondary axis.

4. Select the **Turnover** data series and change the chart type to 2D clustered column, for that data series only.

5. In the plot area, display the image **money** from the data files.

6. Without changing any data, change the scale of the **Value Axis** (Turnover) so that it is displayed in **Thousands** with a major unit setting of **5000**.

7. Without changing any data, change the scale of the **Secondary Value Axis** (Profit) so that it is displayed in **Thousands** and starts at **10,000**.

8. Change the font of all the text and numbers on the chart to **Verdana**.

9. Move the **Legend** to inside the plot area.

10. Apply an entrance animation effect of **Dissolve In** to the chart.

11. Amend the options for the effects on the slide so that the following sequence is obtained during a slide show:

    | First click | Chart background and axes appear |
    | Second click | Turnover Data Series appears |
    | Third click | Profit Data Series appears |

12. Save the presentation as **Chart2** and close it.

## Exercise 9

1.  Start a new presentation containing a blank **Title and Content** slide and select the **Insert Chart** option. This slide will present the average temperature and rainfall for London over the summer months. Add a title of **London Weather**.

2.  Add a 2D column chart to the slide and replace the data with the data from the following table. If using *2007* make sure that **Rainfall** and **Temperature** are added in the correct position on the datasheet as **series**:

| Summer in London | Apr | May | Jun | Jul | Aug | Sep |
|---|---|---|---|---|---|---|
| Rainfall (cms) | 3.9 | 4.5 | 4.5 | 5.8 | 6.0 | 5.5 |
| Temperature (°C) | 8.0 | 10.0 | 14.0 | 17.0 | 19.0 | 15.0 |

3.  Change the chart type for the **Rainfall** series to a **Line** chart and plot it on a secondary axis.

4.  Add vertical captions of **Rainfall** and **Temperature** to the left and right vertical axes respectively. Move the **Legend** box inside the chart area to the upper right corner and fill it with pale blue.

5.  Set the **Rainfall** axis to have a minimum value of **3** and major divisions on the axis representing **0.2cm**.

6.  Change the gap between the columns to **100**.

7.  Set the **Temperature** axis to have a minimum value of **5** and major divisions on that axis representing **1.0** degree.

8.  Apply a custom animation entrance effect of **Wipe** to the chart.

9.  Amend the **Effect Options** so that the following sequence is obtained during a slide show:

    Before clicking  The chart background and axes are already shown.

    First click     Data for the first month (April) is displayed

    Second click    Data for the second month (May) is displayed

    and so on.

10. Save the presentation as **Weather** and close it.

## Multimedia

These exercises include topics taken from the following list: inserting sounds and movies, changing animation settings, changing animation sequences.

### Exercise 10

1.  Open the presentation **Outdoor**.

2.  On slide **2** insert an animated clip art image to represent **hiking**. If you cannot locate a suitable image from the *Microsoft* Clip Art galleries, insert **hike.gif** from the supplied data files. This has been extracted from the *Microsoft* media collection.

3.  Resize the image so that it is exactly **5cm** high, and maintains the original aspect ratio.

4.  Position the image to be **17cm** from the left edge of the slide and **4cm** from the top edge.

5.  Insert an animated clip art image to represent **climbing**. If you cannot locate a suitable image from the *Microsoft* Clip Art galleries, insert **climb.gif** from the supplied data files. This has also been extracted from the *Microsoft* media collection. Resize the image to be **5cm** high, **17cm** from the left and **10cm** from the top.

6.  Apply custom animation to the slide. Add the following entrance effects, all effects to be activated by mouse click:

    | | |
    |---|---|
    | Title | Faded Swivel |
    | Bullet Text | Wipe, from left, by 1st level paragraphs |
    | Images | Dissolve In |

7. Change the animation sequence to: title, then first bullet text line, then hiking image, then the second bullet text line, then the climbing image.

8. Change the timing so that the title animation starts automatically as the slide opens.

9. Change the timing so that the hiking image appears automatically **1** second after the first bullet text line and then the climbing image appears automatically **1** second after the second bullet text line.

10. Add a sound effect of **chime** to the **hiking** image animation, <u>without</u> inserting a further sound file to the slide.

11. Similarly add a sound effect of **wind** to the **climbing** image animation.

12. Apply settings so that both bullet text lines change to orange when the next animation starts.

13. Show the slide in **Slide Show** view to check the effects.

14. Save the presentation as **Outdoor2**.

15. Close the presentation.

## Exercise 11

1. Open the presentation **Sanctuary**.

2. Insert the sound **Scary** from the supplied data files.

3. Make sure the sound will play automatically.

4. In custom animation, set the sound to start playing at the same time as the previous event, and to loop continuously until the end of the slide. Make sure the sound icon is not seen on the slide.

5. Insert the movie **ghost** from the supplied data files. Make sure the movie will run automatically and will loop continuously.

6. In custom animation, set the movie to start playing **1** second after the previous event, and to stop running when the mouse is clicked.

7. Apply an entrance effect of **Fly In** to the lower text box, started by a mouse click.

8. Insert the sound **Laugh** from the supplied data files to play automatically. In custom animation, set the sound to start playing at the same time as the previous event (Shape 2/ Text Box 10) and not to repeat. Make sure the sound icon is not seen on the slide.

9. Play the slide. The title should animate with sound, then the movie will start moving.

10. Click the mouse to stop the animation and bring in the lower text with new sound.

11. Save the presentation as **Sanctuary2** and close it.

## Exercise 12

1. Open the presentation **Captains**.

2. Insert a new slide at the end of the presentation that will contain a title and some text. Add a title of **New Attraction – Scuba Diving**.

3. Enter two lines of text, **Swim with the exotic creatures of the Coral Reefs**, and **Click to see simulation**.

4. In the area at the right of the slide, insert the movie **fish** from the supplied data files to play automatically.

5. Change the **Effect Options** so that the movie requires a mouse click to start and will loop until the mouse is clicked again. The object is to be hidden when it is not playing.

6. Insert the sound file **Underwater** from the supplied data files so that it plays automatically.

7. Animate the sound to start at the same time as the **fish** animation and to loop until the mouse is next clicked. The sound icon is to be hidden.

8. Show the slide in **Slide Show** view. Click once to start the animation and sound, click again (away from the movie) to stop them both. End the show.

9. Save the presentation as **Captains2** and close it.

## Slide Shows

These exercises include topics taken from the following list: creating and editing action buttons, creating and editing custom shows, running a custom show, applying slide transitions, applying timings, setting up a slide show.

## Exercise 13

1. Open the presentation **Henderson**.

2. Apply a slide transition of **Dissolve** to all slides.

3. Adjust the settings so that <u>each</u> slide will appear after a delay of **5** seconds, but clicking the mouse button will cause the transition to start immediately. Make sure this is applied to all slides.

4. Change the speed for <u>all</u> transitions to **Slow**.

5. Remove the transition timing from the first slide only so that the first slide will remain on screen permanently until the mouse is clicked.

6.  Add a hyperlink on the last bullet point text on slide **5** which will link to the presentation **Products** in the supplied data files folder.

7.  Select **Welcomes New Starters** on slide **1** and add an entrance animation of **Fly In**, to start **2** seconds after the slide opens.

8.  Save the presentation as **Henderson2** but leave it open.

9.  Change the transition timings to **7** seconds for <u>every</u> slide.

10. Create a **Custom Show** called **Rolling**, to include slides **1, 3, 4, 5, 11, 15**.

11. Set up a slide show to show the **Rolling** custom show as a continuously looping show to be viewed at a kiosk. The show should run automatically without any intervention and animations are <u>not</u> to be displayed.

12. Amend the **Rolling** custom show to include the original slide **14, Summary**. Change the position of the new slide in the custom show so that it is the penultimate slide, i.e. before the **Message** slide.

13. Check the operation of the **Rolling** custom show.

14. Create a copy of the **Rolling** custom show, naming it **Rolling2**.

15. Delete the **Rolling** custom show.

16. Save the presentation as **Henderson3** and close it.

## Exercise 14

1.  Open the presentation **Henderson**.

2.  On slide **9, Benefits Review**, insert a hyperlink on the last text line which links to the document **Handbook** which is included in the supplied data files.

3.  On slide **14, Summary**, change the hyperlink on the last text line so that it now links to the web site **www.ciasupport.co.uk**. This link can only be tested if an active internet connection is available on your computer.

4. On slide **2**, **Topics**, insert a hyperlink on the first bulleted text line which will link to slide **3**.

5. Similarly insert a hyperlink on the second bulleted text line which will link to slide **7**, a hyperlink on the third bulleted text line which will link to slide **11**, and a hyperlink on the last bulleted text line which will link to slide **14**.

6. Change the link on the second bulleted text line so that it links to slide **8**.

7. Display slide **2** in **Slide Show** view and check the links work correctly. Use the navigation controls to return to slide **2** each time.

8. Edit the colour scheme for the presentation so that hyperlinks and followed hyperlinks are both shown as white text. What feature remains to indicate which text lines on slides are hyperlinks?

9. Create a **Custom** action button in the lower left of slide **8**, **Terms of Employment**. Enter settings so that the button hyperlinks back to slide **2**. Add a caption of **Topics** to the button.

10. Create identical buttons on slides **11**, **Attitude** and **14**, **Summary**. Use copy and paste if desired.

11. On slide **5**, **Main Products**, add another bullet text line **New Projects**. Add a hyperlink to the line which links to slide **6**, **New Projects**. Hide slide **6** from appearing in the slide show sequence.

12. Set up a slide show which will be presented by a speaker, showing all slides, with animations, but which can only be progressed by using the mouse button.

13. Run the slide show from slide **1** and check all links. On slide **5**, **Main Products**, what are the options for moving forward through the show?

14. Run the show again. At slide **3**, display a black screen.

15. Continue the show to the end.

16. Save the presentation as **Henderson4** and close it.

© CiA Training Ltd 2009

## Exercise 15

1. Open the presentation **Extreme**.

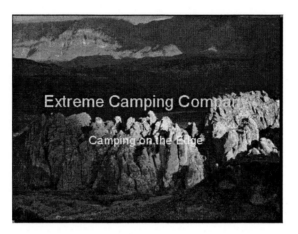

2. Rehearse timings for the presentation and save them for future use, (no need to be too realistic, a few seconds per slide will be adequate).

3. Create a **Custom Show** called **Excursions** which will include slides **1**, **6**, **7**, **8**, **9**, **10**.

4. Insert the slide from the **Further** presentation at the end of the current presentation.

5. Underneath the first bullet point text, type a suitable web site URL and press **<Enter>**. If you do know a suitable URL, type **www.ciasupport.co.uk**.

6. Typing a valid URL may automatically generate a web site hyperlink to that address. If the text is underlined, edit the hyperlink information and check that the correct site address has been used. If the hyperlink is not added automatically, insert the appropriate web site link manually. What does the application add to the typed URL in the dialog box to make the address?

7. Highlight the word **here** in the second bullet point text and add an e-mail address hyperlink. Make the e-mail address **extreme@ciasupport.co.uk** and add a subject of **Reservations**.

8. Edit the **Excursions** custom show to include the new slide.

9. Set up a slide show to be presented by a speaker, showing all slides, no animation and which is advanced by either timings or mouse click.

10. Remove the hyperlink to the web site URL.

11. Remove the transition timings (set to **0** seconds).

12. Run the show and use the pen to write on slide **4, with instructor**. Keep the ink annotation when prompted.

13. Reapply transition timings of **5** seconds to each slide.

14. Save the presentation as **Extreme2** and close it.

## Linking

These exercises include topics taken from the following list: creating a link to a text file, linking to a chart, linking to a worksheet range, modifying linked data, breaking links and embedding data, editing embedded data, saving a slide as an image.

## Exercise 16

1. Open the presentation **Henderson**.

2. Insert a new **Title only** slide after slide **10, Performance Reviews**, and add a title of **Objectives**.

3. As the company objectives are in the process of development it is preferable to link to the appropriate document rather than copy it onto the slide. Why?

4. In the main area of the new slide, insert a link to the file **Objectives** which is included in the supplied data file folder. Do not display as an icon.

5. Save the presentation as **Links1** and close it.

6. Open **Objectives** in *Word* and add another bulleted line: **increase profitability of the company year on year**. Save the file.

7. Open the **Links1** presentation, taking the option to update the links. Check that slide **11** shows the new text.

8.  This is now the final version of the objectives. Break the link to **Objectives**, save the presentation as **Links2**, and close it.

9.  Open **Links2**. How can you tell there are no longer any active automatic links in the presentation?

10. Insert a new **Title Only** slide after slide **7 Turnover**. Add the title **Turnover Range**.

11. Open the *Excel* file **Turnover** and make sure the **Data** tab is selected. Save the file and close *Excel*.

12. On the new slide, insert (embed) the data from **Turnover**.

13. Change the **2008** figure for **Other** to **23.5**.

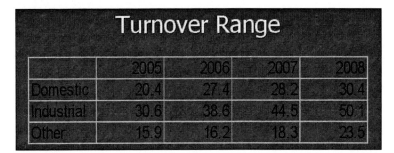

| Turnover Range | | | | |
|---|---|---|---|---|
| | 2005 | 2006 | 2007 | 2008 |
| Domestic | 20.4 | 27.4 | 28.2 | 30.4 |
| Industrial | 30.6 | 38.6 | 44.5 | 50.1 |
| Other | 15.9 | 16.2 | 18.3 | 23.5 |

14. The embedded data is not actually needed in this presentation. Delete the **Turnover Range** slide.

15. Close the presentation, <u>without</u> saving.

16. Remove the added text from the **Objectives** document and save it. Close **Objectives** and *Word*.

## Exercise 17

1.  Open the presentation **Extreme**.

2.  Insert two new **Title only** slides at the end of the presentation and add titles of **Reservations** and **Prices**.

3.  Open the workbook **Bookings** in *Excel*. Copy the data range **A1:D17** from **Sheet1** and paste it to the **Reservations** slide as a linked object.

4.  Resize the object so that the data is clearly legible.

5.  Similarly include the data range **A1:C5** from **Sheet2** as a link on the **Prices** slide and resize it.

6.  Save the presentation as **Extreme3** and close it.

7.  In *Excel,* change one or two cells of data in **Sheet 1** and **Sheet 2**, then change the background colour of both data areas from yellow to pale green. Save and close the workbook.

8.  Open the presentation **Extreme3**, making sure that the data on slides **11** and **12** is current. If you suspect the source data has changed again, what commands would start the process to ensure the data on the slides is up to date, <u>without</u> opening and closing the presentation?

9.  The price data is now considered fixed. Change the object on slide **12**, **Prices**, so that it is embedded rather than linked.

10. Save slide **12** as an image file **Pricelist.gif**.

11. Save the whole presentation again as **Extreme3** and close it.

## Exercise 18

1.  Open the workbook **Turnover** in *Excel* and make sure the chart tab is selected. Save and close.

2.  Open the presentation **Henderson**.

3.  Delete the chart from slide **7**, **Turnover**, and replace it with a link to the chart in the workbook **Turnover**, which is included in the supplied data folder. If **Turnover** and *Excel* were opened in the process, close them now.

4.  In the presentation, increase the size of the chart so that it occupies most of the available space.

5.  Double click the linked chart to open the source workbook in *Excel*.

6.  On the **Data** sheet add a new column for 2009.

| 2009 |
|------|
| 35   |
| 50   |
| 25   |

7.  Select the **Chart** tab in the workbook and check that it shows the extra data then save the workbook.

8.  Check that the chart in the presentation now shows the amended data and resize it again if necessary.

9.  Change the properties of the link so that it will no longer update automatically, but will require manual updates. Save the presentation as **Links3** and close it.

10. In the **Turnover** workbook, change the **Wall** colour of the chart to light blue, then save and close it. Close *Excel*.

11. Open the **Links3** presentation.

12. By manually updating the link, display the chart on slide **7** to show the latest changes.

13. Save all slides in the presentation as an image file named **Links image**, in **.gif** format

14. Save the presentation as **Links3** and close it.

The following revision exercises can involve processes from any part of the ECDL advanced syllabus.

## Exercise 19

1.  Why should you consider the target audience for a presentation?

    a) You need to be aware of their subject knowledge.

    b) The tone should be right for the audience.

    c) Both a and b.

    d) Neither a nor b.

2.  Which of the following sentences is true?

    a) It doesn't matter what colour background you use.

    b) The text should always be light on a dark background.

    c) The text should always be dark on a light background.

    d) The text should be legible against the background.

3.  Open the presentation **Traditions**. Apply the design template **Compass** (**Apex** in *2007*) and save as **Traditions2**.

4.  Change the background colour of the image on slide **1** (you will need to click the image twice to edit it, but do not double click) to match the colour of the slide background as much as possible. Enlarge the image until the dragon's tail overlaps the text, but ensure the text is not obscured by the image (select **Draw | Order | Send to Back**; in *2007* from the **Arrange** group select **Send to Back**).

5.  On slide **2**, resize the graphic to twice its original size. Position it at **16.5cm** horizontally and **4.5cm** vertically from the top left corner of the slide.

6.  Change the background colour of the sky to dark blue. Ensure the sun is not obscured as a result.

7.  Apply the sound **china** from the data files to slide **1** (this is a copy of a sound file supplied with *Office*). Ensure the sound plays automatically, but that it stops after the current slide. Drag the icon to the bottom left corner of the slide.

8.  Apply animation to the dragon image so that it pinwheels in (**Exciting** effect). Ensure it starts at the same time as the music.

9.  On slide **4** apply the same entrance effect of **Rise Up** to the images, triggered by mouse click, so they enter the slide in the following order: **rooster, dog, boar, rat, ox, tiger, rabbit, dragon, snake, horse, sheep, monkey**.

10. Save slide **4** as an image in **.png** format to the location where the data is saved, naming it **creatures.png**.

11. After slide **5**, insert all slides from the **Creatures** presentation. Apply a **bounce** entrance animation effect to the graphic on each of the new slides.

12. Create a custom show called **Overview** from slides **2, 3, 18-22**.

13. Attach a custom action button to the bottom right corner of slide **1** to run the custom show.

14. Add the text **Main Points** to the button. Resize the button so the text fits neatly. Change the colour of the button to gold and the text to the same colour as the slide background.

15. Apply timings to the show, allowing adequate time for the text to be read and the graphics to be brought in. Do <u>not</u> view the custom show while rehearsing timings.

16. Insert a blank slide at the end of the show and apply a timing of **5** seconds to it. Ensure the show is set up to use timings and then view the slide show (not the custom show at this stage).

17. Pause at slide **10** (**Ox**), then continue the show.

18. When the show ends, start it again, this time viewing the custom show. Continue to view the rest of the presentation.

19. Save the presentation with the same name (**Traditions2**) and close it.

## Exercise 20

1. Open the presentation **Favourites** and add **Favourites** as the title and your name as the subtitle on the first slide.

2. Insert the image **lake** on to slide **2** and resize it to **10cms** high, maintaining the original proportions.

3. Adjust the contrast of the image, reducing it by **3** levels.

4. Use **Align and Distribute** tools to make sure that the image is positioned exactly in the centre of the slide (horizontally and vertically).

5. Add a right aligned text box underneath the image with the text **Derwentwater from Friars Crag**.

6. Insert the image **Kitten** on to slide **3**. Crop the picture until it just shows the kitten's face, then resize the resulting image to about **8cm** square.

7. Copy the image and paste it three times so that there are four identical images on the slide.

8. Convert one image to **Black and White**, one to **Grayscale**, and one to **Washout**. Arrange the images from left to right in the order **Black and White, Washout, Grayscale**, with the original image on the far right. Don't worry that the images overlap.

9. Use **Align and Distribute** tools to distribute the images evenly across the slide both horizontally and vertically, i.e. from top left to bottom right, again don't worry about the overlap.

10. Apply any entrance animation effect to all four images on the slide.

11. Edit the effects so that the entrance of the top left image is triggered by a mouse click, then each of the other images appears automatically in turn at 2 second intervals.

12. Insert the image **Car** as an embedded object on to slide **4**. Reduce the size of the image and move it to the left of the slide.

13. Insert the image **Car** again. Reduce the size of the image and move it to the right of the slide if necessary to ensure that both images are displayed side by side on the slide.

14. Distribute the two images horizontally across the slide.

15. Use a format copying tool to apply the style from the **Lake** image on slide **2** to the two images on slide **4**. What is the name of the tool used?

16. Apply a blue tissue paper background texture effect to all slides.

17. Save all slides in the presentation as an image in **.gif** format, named **Favourites image**.

18. Save the presentation as **Favourites2** and close it.

## Exercise 21

1. Open the presentation **Forest Lodge**.

2. Amend the master slides as follows: on the **Slide Master**, change the master text style to **Tempus Sans ITC 32pt** and the second level text to **Tempus Sans ITC 28pt**. Ensure the **Title Master**, subtitle style is **Tempus Sans ITC 32pt**.

3. Apply a new set of colours (colour scheme or theme colours) to all slides. Choose a set with a pale green background, e.g the $5^{th}$ scheme.

4. Create a custom slide master, using the fonts mentioned above (**Master Title style Tempus Sans ITC 44pt**), but use a pale blue colour scheme.

5. Apply the custom slide master to slide **9 Testimonials**.

6. The image on all non-title slides needs to be changed. Replace the tree image on the slide master and the custom slide master with the **forest** image from the data files.

7. On slide **3**, change the format of the pyramid diagram to a preset **gradient** format.

8. The table on slide **7** has been inserted as an image. Print this slide only for reference. Delete the image and change the slide layout to **Title and Content**.

9. Re-enter the data for weekly prices as a table. If the image is obscured by the table, resize the table proportionately to prevent this. Centre all text in the table and apply teal (green/blue) coloured shading to row 1 and column 1.

10. On slide **8**, view the data associated with the chart (on the **Data** sheet) and change the year range from **1998-2003** to **2004-2009**. Change the colour of the data series to dark green and display the image **ivy** on the chart walls. The image can be found in the supplied data files

11. Change the fonts on the chart to **Tempus Sans ITC 16pt** and change the gap width of the data series to **200**.

12. Remove the **Price List** slide from the **Public** custom show.

13. On slide **9**, create a hyperlink from the text **Click here to read actual testimonials** to the **Testimonial** document from the data files.

14. Apply a **Diamond** entrance effect to the **Forest Lodge** title on slide **1**, triggered by a mouse click. Edit the effect options so that the text dims to pale green after animation.

15. Apply a **Fade Smoothly** transition to all slides in the show and apply numbers to all slides.

16. Ensure the slide show is set up to be advanced manually, rather than by using timings.

17. View the show without viewing the custom show (via the **Demo** button on slide **1**). Test the link on slide **9**, then close *Word*.

18. View the **Public** custom show then copy the **Public** custom show and name it **Public Copy**.

19. Save the presentation as **Forest Lodge2** and close it.

## Exercise 22

1. Open the presentation **Egypt Tours**.

2. Apply a design template of **Cliff** (**Trek** theme in *2007*) to the slide and title master.

3. Apply a new set of colours (colour scheme or theme colours) to all masters.

4. On the slide master, change the master title style to **Papyrus 44pt**, master text style to **Papyrus 32pt** and the second level text to **Papyrus 28pt**. Ensure the fonts on the title master have also changed to **Papyrus**.

5. Delete the date/time placeholder. If using *2007*, right align the title and subtitle on the title master and the title on the slide master.

6. Insert the **profile** graphic to appear as a logo in the top left corner of all slides, including title slides. Resize the graphic to approximately **3.9cm x 2.6cm**.

7. Use the **Picture** toolbar (**Adjust** group in *2007*) to set the white background of this image as a transparent colour.

8. On slide **1**, insert the sound file **desert** from the supplied data folder. Ensure it plays automatically, continuously throughout the presentation and that its icon is hidden when not being played.

9. Apply any custom animation effect, animated on mouse click, medium speed, to the text, but not the title, on each slide.

10. Apply a second effect to each graphic on slides **3** to the end (not the logo), so that the text comes in 3 seconds before the graphic.

11. On slide **2**, create a new bullet point **Visit the touregypt web site**. Create a hyperlink from this text to the **www.touregypt.net** URL.

12. The tour operator has informed you that the **Cairo Museum** is closed for refurbishment. Hide slide **3**.

13. Rehearse timings for the presentation.

14. Create a new slide **14** to contain a title and a pyramid diagram. Add the title **Egypt Tours show you**.

15. Create a pyramid diagram, reading from bottom to top **History**, **Treasures**, **Culture**.

16. Set up the show to run using timings. View the show, then save it as **Egypt Tours2**.

17. Create a custom show called **Offers** which includes the slides **1, 2, 7, 9, 11, 13**. Run the custom show without using the **Set Up Show** dialog box. Which dialog box or button will be used?

18. Save and close the presentation.

## Exercise 23

1. Start a new blank presentation and apply the design template **Crayons** (**Oriel** theme if using *2007*). The presentation is to promote a further education centre, Chipperstone College.

2. Insert text from the file **Outline**.

3. Change the layout of slide **2** to **Title Slide** and delete slide **1**.

4. Change the size of the master title style to **40pt**, master text style to **28pt** and second level text to **24pt**.

5.  Insert the following images from file on to slides **4** to **10**, positioning them at the bottom right of the slide and ensuring they do not obscure any part of the slide design graphics:

*Note:*   *In XP and 2003, ensure automatic layout is deactivated before inserting the images. Select **Tools | AutoCorrect Options** and the **AutoFormat As You Type** tab. If **Automatic layout for inserted objects** is checked, remove the check and click **OK**. It can be reactivated later if desired.*

Slide 4 - **computer** increase the brightness by **3** levels

Slide 5 - **business**

Slide 6 - **beauty**

Slide 7 - **diy**

Slide 8 - **literature**

Slide 9 - **science**

Slide 10 - **telephone** (flip the phone image horizontally).

6.  Insert a new **Title Only** slide immediately after slide **3 Courses on Offer**. Add the title **Pass Rates**.

7.  Paste in the chart from the *Excel* workbook **Passes**, ensuring it is linked to the source information.

8.  Save the presentation as **College** and close it.

9.  Open the **Passes** workbook and change the figures for 2004 to **60** in the **Data** sheet. Save the workbook, but leave it open.

10. Reopen the presentation **College** and update the link. Close **Passes**.

11. Break the link to the workbook.

12. Apply an entrance effect of **Checkerboard** to the chart, medium speed, advanced on mouse click.

13. To each text frame containing bullets, apply an entrance effect of **Fly In From Bottom**, speed fast, so that each line is animated separately. On slide **3**, animate each second level line separately and dim each one to blue after animation.

14. On slide **11**, animate the names to come in 2 seconds after the previous effect.

15. Apply an **Uncover Right** transition, medium speed, to all slides.

16. Run the slide show.

17. Reorder animation for the courses on slide **3** so they appear in alphabetical order.

18. Apply timings to the presentation and set it up to use these timings.

19. Run the show again to check the settings, then save the presentation with the same name and close it.

1. Start a new, blank presentation, which is to be used as the template for a presentation to promote the local fencing club, The CiA Sabres. Set up the master slides as follows:

    **Background** - preset **Gradient** fill effect of **Parchment**, shaded from the title.

    **Slide master** - master title style **Tahoma 44pt**, italic, shadowed; master text style **Tahoma 24pt**, picture bullet; second level text **Tahoma 20pt**, different picture bullet

    **Title master** - master subtitle style **Tahoma 30pt**

    **Slide numbers** on all slides.

    Delete the date/time placeholder, move the slide number placeholder to the bottom centre and ensure the number is centre aligned.

2. The image **fencer** is to be used on all slides. On the slide master it is to be positioned **0cm** horizontally and **15.56cm** vertically from the top left corner of the slide. On the title master <u>only</u>, it is to be positioned at **0cm** from the top left corner, both horizontally and vertically. Don't forget to hide background graphics on the title master in 2007.

3. Use the **Set Transparent Color** tool to make the white area of the image transparent on all masters, then save the file as a template named **Fencers** and close it.

4. Start a new presentation based on the **Fencers** template. Add the title **The CiA Sabres** and the subtitle **An introduction to our club**. Create the rest of the presentation content by inserting the outline **Sabres**.

5. On slide **4 Equipment**, insert the graphic **mask**. Position it at **15.5cm** horizontally and **8cm** vertically from the top left corner and make the white area transparent. Increase the contrast of the image by **2** levels.

6. Omit the background image on slide **5 Progression**.

7. Change the layout to **Title Only** and use drawing tools to create a flowchart, illustrating the progression from **Foil** to **Epee** to **Sabre**. Link the flowchart shapes with arrows. Align the shapes and arrows centrally on the slide and then distribute them so they are evenly spaced horizontally.

8. Change the fill of the flowchart shapes to a pale gold colour.

9. On the same slide, insert the graphics **foil** and **epee**. Position **foil** at the left of the flowchart and **epee** at the right. Make the white area of the **foil** graphic transparent.

10. On the title master only, animate the fencer image to come in with a fast **Magnify** effect with the rest of the slide content.

11. Use the slide master to animate all slide titles to come in with a fast **Fly In** effect, from **Bottom-Right** and the remaining text to come in after the title with the same effect. All animations to start on mouse click.

12. On slide **4** animate the graphic to **Spiral In** fast after the text. On slide **5** animate the graphics (**foil** first) to spiral in fast. All animations to be activated on mouse click.

13. On slide **9 Club Information** insert the image **kit**. Position it at **16.5cm** horizontally and **6.43cm** vertically from the top left corner. Set the white area as transparent and crop the top part of the graphic so that nothing above the mask is displayed.

14. Create a hyperlink from the e-mail address text on the slide to **info@ciasupport.co.uk**, with a subject of **Reservations**.

15. On slide **4**, create a link from the mask image to the following website: **www.leonpaul.com** (a provider of fencing equipment and information). When setting up the link, create a screen tip - **Visit a supplier**.

16. Insert a new **Title Only** slide after slide **8 Sabre** with the title **Demo**. Insert the movie file **Championship**, to play automatically.

*Note:    Video clip supplied by permission of Leon Paul.*

17. Rehearse timings and set up the show to use them. Which menu command and option would you select to suppress animation in a presentation?

18. View the slide show. Pause at slide **4 Equipment** and annotate the slide with the pen: **Free of charge**. Continue to the end of the show and discard the ink annotation if prompted

19. Save the presentation as **Club** and close it. Delete the template **Fencer**.

This section contains answers to all specific questions posed in the preceding exercises, together with the name of the file or files containing the worked solution for each exercise.

## Exercise 1

Step 1   (d) They are all valid reasons.

Step 2   (c) Although you could make an argument for b or d.

Step 3   Advantages – Grabs attention, makes an impact, more likely to be remembered.
Disadvantages – Distracts focus from the content, may offend or annoy viewers.

Step 4   They can make the presentation more difficult to read and less clear. Moving items can detract from the text.

Step 5   Visibility, (no yellow text on white backgrounds).

Consider colour vision impairments.

Aesthetics, (no purple text on lime green backgrounds).

Step 6   Room size, room layout, lighting, available equipment

Step 7   (a)

Step 8   (c)

## Exercise 2

Step 2   Because we now have dark text on a dark background.

A sample solution for this exercise is saved as **Cruises2 Solution** in the **Solutions** folder.

## Exercise 3

A sample solution for this exercise is saved as **Rocky2 Solution** in the **Solutions** folder.

## Exercise 4

A sample solution for this exercise is saved as **Camping2 Solution** in the **Solutions** folder.

## Exercise 5

A sample solution for this exercise is saved as **Camping3 Solution** in the **Solutions** folder.

## Exercise 6

A sample solution for this exercise is saved as **Tours Solution** in the **Solutions** folder.

## Exercise 7

A sample solution for this exercise is saved as **Diagrams Solution** in the **Solutions** folder.

## Exercise 8

Step 4

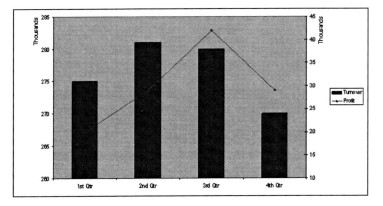

A sample solution for this exercise is saved as **Chart2 Solution** in the **Solutions** folder.

## Exercise 9

A sample solution for this exercise is saved as **Weather Solution** in the **Solutions** folder.

## Exercise 10

A sample solution for this exercise is saved as **Outdoor2 Solution** in the **Solutions** folder.

## Exercise 11

A sample solution for this exercise is saved as **Sanctuary2 Solution** in the **Solutions** folder.

## Exercise 12

A sample solution for this exercise is saved as **Captains2 Solution** in the **Solutions** folder.

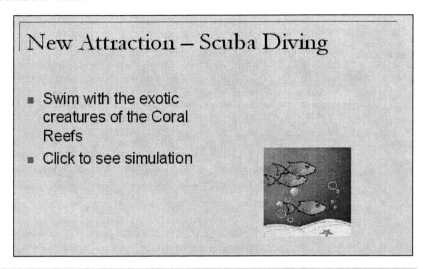

## Exercise 13

Step 12 **Slide Show | Custom Shows**, select **Rolling** from the list and click the **Show** button. In *2007* select the **Slide Show** tab, click **Custom Slide Show** and select **Rolling**.

Or

**Slide Show | Setup Show**, select **Custom show** within the Show slides area, and select **Rolling** from the list. Click **OK** then select **View | Slide Show**. In *2007* select the **Slide Show** tab, click **Set Up Slide Show** and from the **Start Slide Show** group click **From Beginning**.

Examples of the output from this exercise are saved as **Henderson2 Solution** and **Henderson3 Solution** in the **Solutions** folder.

## Exercise 14

Step 8   Text with hyperlinks is underlined.

Step 13 Click on the **New Projects** link to move to slide **6**, or click anywhere else to move to slide **7** with slide **6** hidden.

A sample solution for this exercise is saved as **Henderson4 Solution** in the **Solutions** folder.

## Exercise 15

Step 6   **http://** is added to make the address.

Step 7

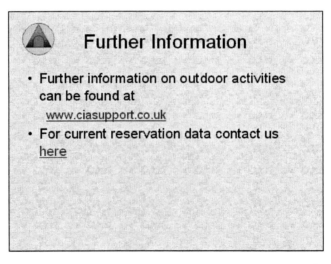

A sample solution for this exercise is saved as **Extreme2 Solution** in the **Solutions** folder.

## Exercise 16

Step 3    So that the presentation will always show the most recent version of the document.

Step 9    Because there is no prompt to update links when the presentation opens.

Examples of the output from this exercise are saved as **Links1 Solution** and **Links2 Solution** in the **Solutions** folder.

## Exercise 17

Step 8    **Edit | Links**. In *2007*, click the **Office Button**, select **Prepare**, then **Edit Links to Files**.

Step 10

A sample solution for this exercise is saved as **Extreme3 Solution** in the **Solutions** folder.

## Exercise 18

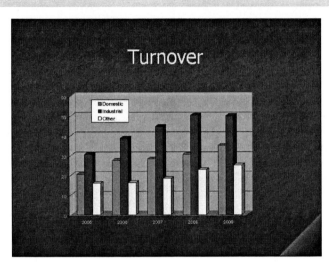

A sample solution for this exercise is saved as **Links3 Solution** in the **Solutions** folder.

## Exercise 19

Step 1    c) They are both valid reasons.

Step 2    d)

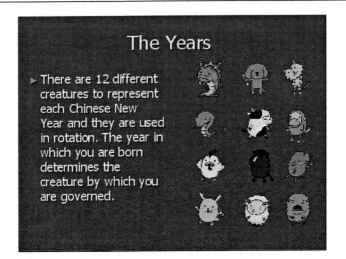

A sample solution for this exercise is saved as **Traditions2 Solution** in the **Solutions** folder.

## Exercise 20

Step 15 **Format Painter**.

A sample solution for this exercise is saved as **Favourites2 Solution** in the **Solutions** folder.

## Exercise 21

Step 8

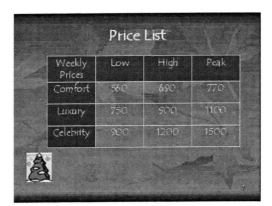

*This shows the PowerPoint XP solution.*

A sample solution for this exercise is saved as **Forest Lodge2 Solution** in the **Solutions** folder.

## Exercise 22

Step 17 The custom show can be run from the **Custom Shows** dialog box or by clicking the **Custom Slide Show** button in 2007.

A sample solution for this exercise is saved as **Egypt Tours2 Solution** in the **Solutions** folder.

## Exercise 23

Step 5 (example slide)

XP/2003                                        2007

A sample solution for this exercise is saved as **College Solution** in the **Solutions** folder.

## Exercise 24

Step 17   Select **Slide Show | Set Up Show** and then check **Show without animation**.

In *2007*, select **Set Up Slide Show** from the **Slide Show** tab then check **Show without animation**.

A sample solution for this exercise is saved as **Club Solution** in the **Solutions** folder.

## *Other Products from CiA Training*

CiA Training Ltd is a leading publishing company, which has consistently delivered the highest quality products since 1985. A wide range of flexible and easy to use self teach resources has been developed by CiA's experienced publishing team to aid the learning process. These include the following ECDL Foundation approved products at the time of publication.

- **ECDL/ICDL Syllabus 5.0**

- **ECDL/ICDL Advanced Syllabus 2.0**

- **ECDL/ICDL Revision Series**

- **ECDL/ICDL Advanced Syllabus 2.0 Revision Series**

- **e-Citizen**

Previous syllabus versions also available - contact us for further details.

We hope you have enjoyed using our materials and would love to hear your opinions about them. If you'd like to give us some feedback, please go to:

**www.ciatraining.co.uk/feedback.php**

and let us know what you think.

New products are constantly being developed. For up to the minute information on our products, to view our full range, to find out more, or to be added to our mailing list, visit:

**www.ciatraining.co.uk**